READING
Triumphs

Mc Graw Hill **Macmillan McGraw-Hill**

RFB&D
learning through listening

Students with print disabilities may be eligible to obtain an accessible, audio version of the pupil edition of this textbook. Please call Recording for the Blind & Dyslexic at 1-800-221-4792 for complete information.

B

The *McGraw·Hill* Companies

Macmillan
McGraw-Hill

Published by Macmillan/McGraw-Hill, of McGraw-Hill Education, a division of
The McGraw-Hill Companies, Inc., Two Penn Plaza, New York, New York 10121.

Printed in the United States of America

ISBN 0-02-194826-7

10 11 12 13 14 RJE 14 13 12 11 10

C O N T E N T S

Unit 3

Unit 6

Working with Words

Phonics

Read the words.

bake	ate	slip
cake	lake	made
glad	make	grape
plane	Jake	game

Words to Know

Read the words.

eat	walk
said	all

Time to Read

Read the story.

Fox and Grapes

Fox had grapes.
"Can I eat?" asked Hen.
"Walk to me," said Fox
But then Fox ate them all!

7

Dave and Kate

by Lana Rios

illustrated by José Cruz

Dave and Kate make things.
What can they make?

Dave and Kate made this!
They will live in it.

Kate and Dave made a pet.
It can **walk** and run fast!

Kate and Dave made a plane.
What will they make next?

"Let's go up!" said Kate.
"This is the best thing yet!"

Comprehension Check

Retell

Retell the story.
Use the pictures.

Think About It

1. Who is the story about?
2. Where do you think Kate and Dave will go in their rocket?

Write About It

Write about something you would like to make.

Jake's Cake

by Beth Lewis

Illustrated by Olga and Aleksey Ivanov

Jake will bake a cake.
His pals will help him.

"Let's add eggs," said Jane.

"Let's add nuts," said Ed.

Jake mixed and mixed.

In went the cake.
Then Jake and his pals sat.

"What a cake!" said Jane.
"It's just grand!"

"Let's eat!" said Jake.

And they ate it all up!

Comprehension Check

Retell

Retell the story.
Use the pictures.

Think About It

1. Where does the story take place?
2. How do the characters act like friends?

Write About It

Write about a food you can help make.

Working with Words

Phonics

Read the words.

scale	skate	rake
skin	skunk	sled
spin	snake	snack
swim	swing	game

Words to Know

Read the words.

was	under
together	when

Time to Read

Read the story.

Skunk at the Lake

I was camping with Dad.
We sat under the hot sun.
Then we swam together.
We ran when a skunk came!
Back to the tent we went!

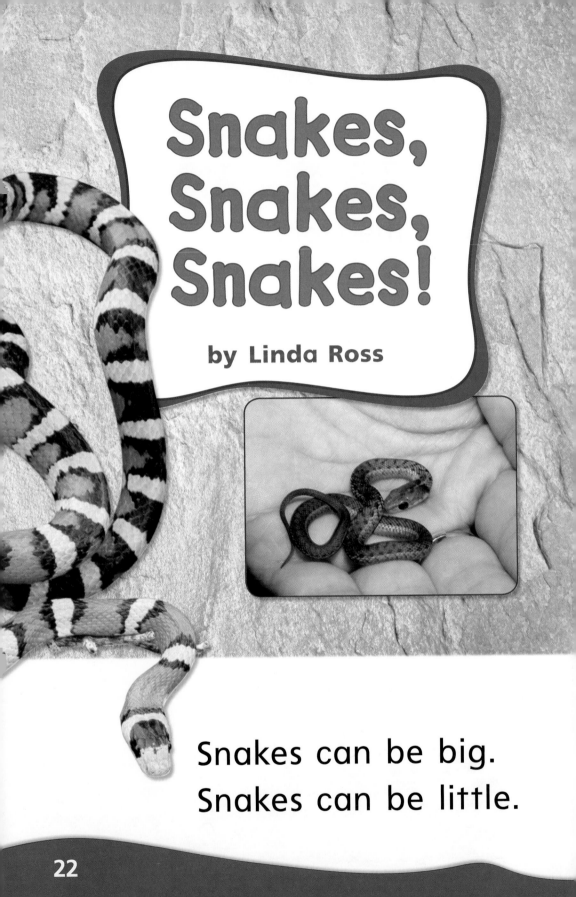

Snakes, Snakes, Snakes!

by Linda Ross

Snakes can be big.
Snakes can be little.

Look at this snake's skin.
It has many scales.

A snake can not run.
A snake has no legs.
But it is fast!

This snake was hot.
It went under a rock.

What do snakes eat?
This snake just ate an egg.
That's a big snack!

Comprehension Check

Retell

Retell the story.
Use the pictures.

Think About It

1. What is this story about?
2. How are all snakes
   the same?

Write About It

What can a snake do?
Write about it.

Kids Can Play

by Bernice Reynolds

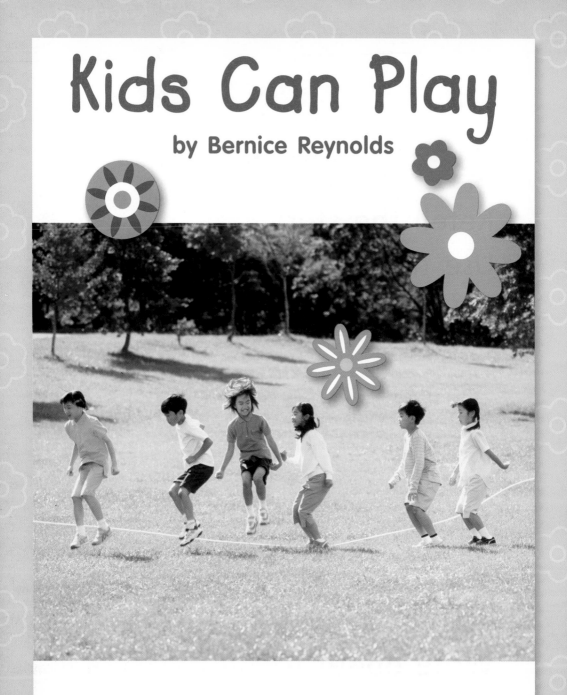

What can kids play?
Let's take a look!

Kids can skate.
They can spin and spin!

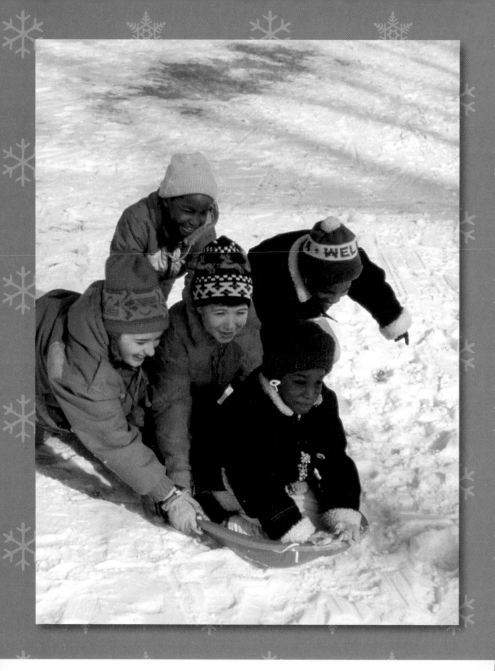

Kids can sled together.
This hill is big.
This sled is fast!

Kids can swim when it's hot.
It's fun to get wet.
Jump in!

Kids can swing.
They go up, up, up!
Kids can have fun!

Comprehension Check

Retell

Retell the story.
Use the pictures.

Think About It

1. What is the story about?
2. What do kids do when it's cold?

Write About It

What do you like to play?

Working with Words

Phonics

Read the words.

bunch	check	chick
chimp	chomp	spill
lunch	sled	munch
when	which	catch

Words to Know

Read the words.

our	some
come	your

Time to Read

Read the story.

Our Mom

We are little chicks. Our mom is a hen. Mom makes some lunch. We come when Mom clucks. Can your mom cluck?

Wake Up, Chicks!

by Emiko Asato

illustrated by
Shari Halpern

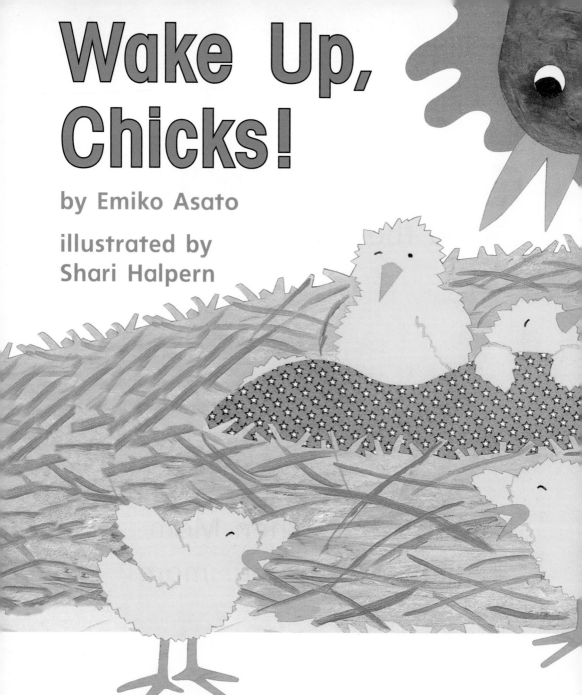

Wake up, little chicks.
Make your bed.

The hot sun is up.
Come and get fed.

A chick is missing!
Which chick can it be?

Come and help, chicks.
Let's check and see.

It's little Mitch.
Mitch is in bed!
Wake up, Mitch!
Come and get fed.

Comprehension Check

Retell

Retell the story.
Use the pictures.

Think About It

1. What happens after the chicks get up?
2. Why do you think Mitch didn't get up?

Write About It

Have you ever not wanted to get up? Write about it.

Let's Eat Lunch

by Lana Rios
illustrated by R. W. Alley

Munch, munch!
Let's eat some lunch.

A chimp has his lunch.
It comes in a bunch.

This is a good lunch.
Crunch, crunch, crunch!

Grass makes a good lunch.
Chomp, chomp, munch!

Munch! Crunch!
Let's eat our lunch!

Comprehension Check

Retell

Retell the story.
Use the pictures.

Think About It

1. What different lunches are in the story?

2. Why is it important to eat a good lunch?

Write About It

Write about how another animal eats lunch.

Working with Words

Phonics

Read the words.

dime	white	dive
fine	five	glide
hide	like	line
mine	chick	time

Words to Know

Read the words.

where	now
how	there

Time to Read

Read the story.

Where Will Pig Hide?

Little Pig likes to hide.
Where will Pig hide now?
Pig will hide in the well.
How will Pig get there?
Look but do not tell!

Five Ducks and a Frog

by Linda Ross

illustrated by Joan Paley

Five ducks swim in a line.

Look at them glide.

They have a fine time.

"Let's play!" said a frog.
"Let's hide in this log."

"Yes! Yes!" said five ducks.
"Let's hide in that log!"

Frog said, "Let's dive!"

"Yes! Yes!" said the five.

Five ducks get back in line.
Frog thinks that is fine.

Now there are six in a line.
Five ducks plus a frog!
They have a fine time.

Comprehension Check

Retell

Retell the story.
Use the pictures.

Think About It

1. What might the frog and ducks do next?
2. Why does the frog get in line at the end?

Write About It

How do the ducks and frog have fun?

Miss White's Dime

by Tasha Wilson

illustrated by Deborah Morse

Where is Miss White's dime?

"I had it," said Miss White.
"It was mine. Where is it?"

"I will help," said Mike.

"How?" asked Miss White.

"I will ask Hen," said Mike.

"What dime?" asked Hen.
"I sit here all the time.
But I did not see a dime."

Mike went back.
Mike looked at Miss White.

"Stand up," said Mike.
"What is in your nest?"

"It is a dime!" said Mike.
"That is just fine!
Miss White sat on her dime."

Comprehension Check

Retell

Retell the story.
Use the pictures.

Think About It

1. Where did you think Mike would find the dime?
2. How do you think the dime ended up in the nest?

Write About It

What have you lost?
Where did you find it?

Working with Words

Phonics

Read the words.

scratch	scrub	fine
Scruff	hide	splash
split	spring	strike
stripe	dive	struck

Words to Know

Read the words.

give	put
of	three

Time to Read

Read the story.

A Bath for Scruff

Let's give Scruff a bath.
I can put in lots of suds.
Scruff likes to splash.
Let's give him three baths!

Stripes, Stripes, Stripes!

by Linda Ross

What has stripes?
Lots of things have stripes.

This flag has stripes.
They are white and red.

This big cat has stripes.
It is black and tan.
It likes to scratch.

This fish has black stripes.
It swims and swims.

See what Ann put on.
Today Ann has stripes.
Ann likes stripes a lot.

Comprehension Check

Retell

Retell the story.
Use the pictures.

Think About It

1. How are the fish and the zebra the same? How are they different?

2. What stripes in this story are made by people?

Write About It

Write about something else that has stripes.

It's Spring!

by Lana Rios
illustrated by Judith Moffatt

In spring, I plant things.
I give the plants a drink.

In spring, I ride a bike.
That is what I like.

In spring, I give Spot a bath.
I scrub and scrub.
Spot likes to splash.

In spring, we make kites.
We put string on them.

Three kites go up, up, up!
We like spring!

Comprehension Check

Retell

Retell the story.
Use the pictures.

Think About It

1. How is riding a bike the same as flying a kite?
2. What is spring like where you live?

Write About It

What do you like to do in spring?

Working with Words

Phonics

Read the words.

chose	hole	home
Mole	splash	nose
poke	rose	those
spring	rope	joke

Words to Know

Read the words.

saw	he
soon	into

Time to Read

Read the story.

Roses for Mom

Cub saw lots of roses.
"Mom likes roses!" he said.
Soon he had a big bunch.
Cub went into the cave.
"I chose them just for you,
Mom!" he said.

77

Mole's Home

by Alice T. Low
illustrated by Olga and Aleksey Ivanov

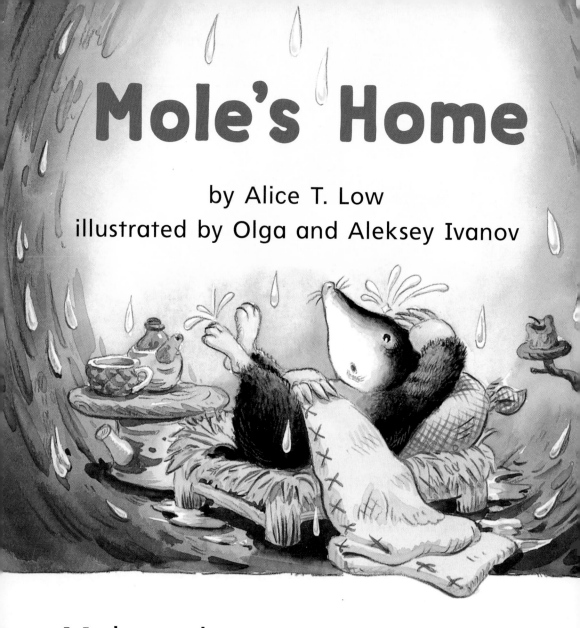

Mole woke up.
Drip, drop! Drip, drop!

"Look at that!" said Mole.
"My home is wet."

"A wet home is not good,"
said Mole. "I'll look for a
good home!"

Mole saw a hole.
Mole poked his nose into it.

"Scat!" said Rat.
"This home is mine!"

Soon Mole saw a den.
He poked his nose in.

"Scat!" said Fox.
"This home is mine!"

Then Mole spotted a cave.
He poked his nose in.

"Scat!" said Cub.
"This home is mine!"

Mole walked on and on.
Then he saw a big hole.
Mole poked his nose in.

"This home is not wet,"
Mole said. "This is a fine
home. I will live here!"

Comprehension Check

Retell

Retell the story.
Use the pictures.

Think About It

1. What is funny about the story ending?
2. Why isn't Mole's home wet at the end?

Write About It

What do you think Mole likes about his home?

Working with Words

Phonics

Read the words.

cute	Duke	flute
home	June	mule
nose	those	cube
tune	use	tube

Words to Know

Read the words.

new	she
could	work

Time to Read

Read the story.

A Singing Mule

Kate got a new mule. She named him Duke. Duke could sing many tunes! He liked to work, too. Duke is a very cute mule!

June's Flute

by Linda B. Ross
illustrated by Carolyn Croll

Dad gave June a flute.

"I like my new flute a lot!" said June.

June went to work with Dad.

"Could I bring my flute?"
she asked.

Dad nodded.

Dad dug and planted.
June helped him.

"Let's stop for a while,"
said Dad.

June and Dad ate lunch.
Then June played a tune.

June's tune made Dad smile.
But that's not all!
Plants popped up when
June played!

"Let's pick them and take
them home," said Dad.

"That is a fine flute!"
said Dad.

"Yes, it is," said June.
"It gives us many things!"

Comprehension Check

Retell

Retell the story.
Use the pictures.

Think About It

1. Why is the flute special?
2. How do June and Dad feel when they see plants popping up?

Write About It

What would you do
with a special flute?

Working with Words

Phonics

Read the words.

cute	day	gray
may	mule	sail
train	way	rain
stay	play	main

Words to Know

Read the words.

read	about
know	these

Time to Read

Read the story.

Let's Sail Away!

I like to read about ships. I know a lot about them. Some of these ships sail for days and days. It's the best way to take a trip!

Trains, Trains, Trains!

by Linda B. Ross

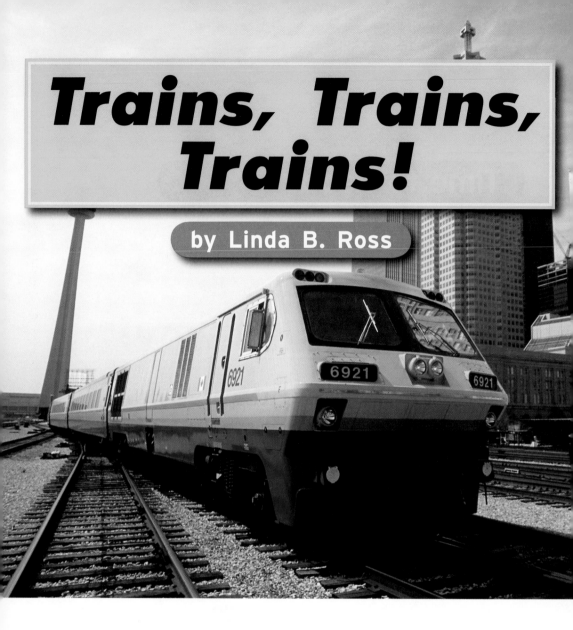

Cling, clang! Cling, clang!
Bells are clanging.
That tells us that a train is
on its way!

You know a lot about trains.
Trains go fast on tracks.
But trains are not as fast as
planes.

A train makes many stops.
You can get on at a stop.
You can get off at a stop.
Let's hop on this train!

What can you do on a train?
You can read.
You can chat with a pal.
You may take a nap!

This train makes long trips.
It has beds.
It can take days to get to
the last stop!

Boxes and crates ride on trains like these.
What do you think is in the boxes and crates?

Will you take a trip on a train?

A train is a good way to go!

Comprehension Check

Retell

Retell the story.
Use the pictures.

Think About It

1. How is a train like a plane?
   How is it different?
2. Why do some trains have
   beds?

Write About It

Write about taking a
pretend trip on a train.

Working with Words

Phonics

Read the words.

be	deep	each
eat	green	may
peach	see	seed
sweet	wait	tree

Words to Know

Read the words.

by	after
down	kind

Time to Read

Read the story.

A Peach Tree

I planted a peach tree by my home. After a while, the tree got big. All day, peaches drop down! It's the best kind of tree!

Let's Plant Seeds

by Lana Rios

illustrated by Philippa A. Kirby

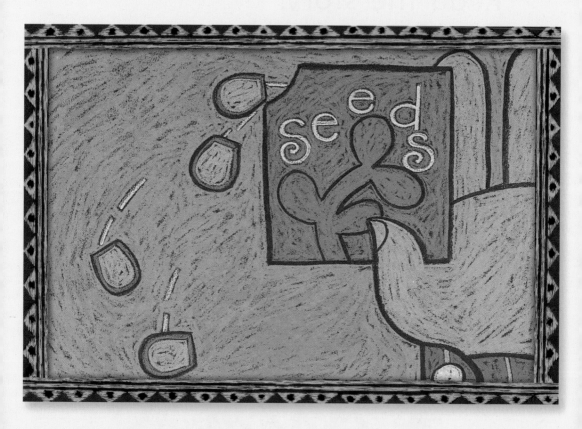

We have some seeds.
What kind can they be?
Let's plant them and see!

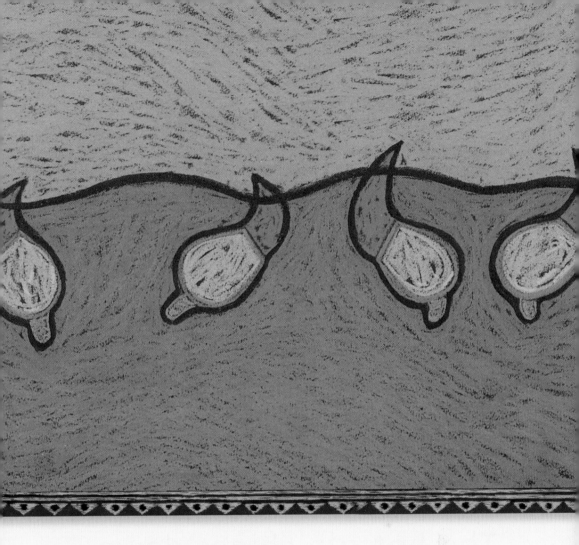

We dig deep holes.
We put the seeds in.
They go side by side.
After that, we wait.

The hot sun shines down.
Sun helps seeds get big.
We see plants come up.

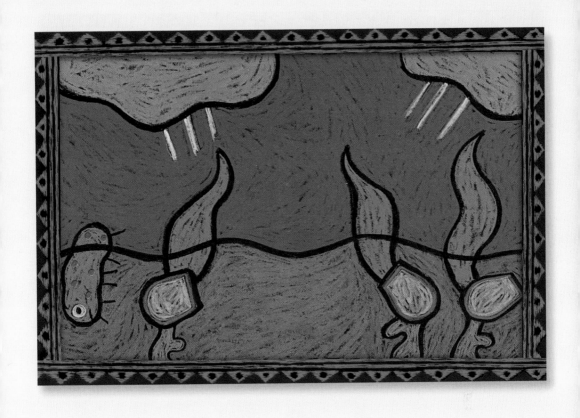

Then it rains.
The plants get big.
We wait and wait.

Look at the plants.
They are big and green!
Soon they will be ripe.
Then we can pick them.

It is a corn plant.
It is time to pick the corn.
We can't wait to eat it!

We take the plants home.
We each get a dish.
Let's eat this sweet plant.
It's such a fine treat!

Comprehension Check

Retell

Retell the story.
Use the pictures.

Think About It

1. What is the story about?
2. What do plants need in order to grow?

Write About It

What kind of seeds
would you like to plant?

Working with Words

Phonics

Read the words.

Buddy	happy	messy
sweet	Milly	puppy
sloppy	sorry	treat
we	silly	funny

Words to Know

Read the words.

before	pull
done	two

Time to Read

Read the story.

My Buddy

I have a puppy named Buddy. I had no pets before Buddy. When we walk, Buddy likes to pull me! When we are done, I give him two treats.

117

Milly Cleans Up

by Beatrice Reynolds
illustrated by Cathy Morrison

"It's still messy in here,"
said Mom.

Mom had asked Milly to
clean up two days before!

But Milly had not done it.

"I am sorry, Mom," Milly said.

Then she got to work!

Milly peeked under the bed.

"It is sloppy!" she said.
"I will fix things up."

Milly gave a pull.

"I missed these!" she yelled.
"Now I can use them!"

Milly kept cleaning.

"I will clean each shelf," she said. "Then I'll fix up my desk."

Then she saw her clock.

"This is my missing clock!" she said. "Now I can tell the time!"

Milly felt happy.

"Cleaning is not that bad," she said. "It's the best way to get your stuff back!"

Comprehension Check

Retell

Retell the story.
Use the pictures.

Think About It

1. How does Milly feel about cleaning at the end?
2. Why does Milly tell her mom she's sorry?

Write About It

Write about a time when you cleaned a room.

Working with Words

Phonics

Read the words.

go	goat	happy
messy	no	show
so	toad	troll
snow	low	boat

Words to Know

Read the words.

their	always
try	over

Time to Read

Read the story.

Five Little Toads

Five little toads go to a pond with their mom. She shows them how to swim.

"You must always kick," she tells them. "Now, let's try to swim over to that rock."

Three Billy Goats

Retold by Linda B. Ross
illustrated by Barry Rockwell

Three Billy Goats wanted to munch on grass. But they had to cross over a bridge. And a mean troll sat under it.

"I will try," said Little Billy.

Trip, trap went his feet.

"Who is that?" yelled the troll.
"You will make a fine meal!"

"Wait for the next Billy Goat," begged Little Billy. "He is so much bigger!"

"Very well!" yelled the troll.

Then Bigger Billy went over.
Trip, trap went his feet.

"You will make such a grand
meal!" yelled the mean troll.

"No! Wait for the next Billy
Goat," begged Bigger Billy. "He
is much, much bigger!"

"Very well!" yelled the troll.

Then Biggest Billy went over.
Trip, trap went his feet.

"I'll eat you!" yelled the troll.

"No!" yelled Biggest Billy.

Biggest Billy gave that mean troll a big kick! Away ran the troll!

Now the three Billy Goats always go over and eat their lunch!

Comprehension Check

Retell

Retell the story.
Use the pictures.

Think About It

1. Could this story really happen? Why or why not?
2. Why did the troll agree to wait for the biggest goat?

Write About It

How would you cross the troll's bridge?

Working with Words

Phonics

Read the words.

by	goat	high
kind	light	my
night	no	right
show	sight	try

Words to Know

Read the words.

every	out
fall	never

Time to Read

Read the story.

Keep Trying!

"Every day, I take my bike out," said Pig. "I try to ride it, but I fall off!"

Pig did not give up. He kept on trying till he got it right! Now he never falls off his bike.

The Light

by Beth Lewis
illustrated by John Wallner

It was night.

"I can't see," said Pig. "My light is out. Can you help me reach it?"

Dog got on top of Pig.

"I can't reach that high," said
Dog. "We need help."

In came Rabbit.

"I will help!" he said.

Rabbit got on top of Dog.

"I can't reach that high," said Rabbit. "We need help."

In came Red.

"I will help!" he said. "But don't fall!"

Red got on top of Rabbit.

"I can't reach it," said Red.
"We need help."

In came Minny.

"Can I try?" she asked.

Minny got on top of Red.

"It's still too high!" said Minny.

In came Frog.

"What a sight this is!" she said. "I will help!"

So Frog got on top of Minny.

"The light is on!" said Frog.

"Thanks so much, my kind pals!" said Pig. "I never could have done it by myself!"

"Now we can read," said Pig.

"Yes, yes! Let's read!" said Pig's pals. "This is fun! Can we do this every night?"

Comprehension Check

Retell

Retell the story.
Use the pictures.

Think About It

1. What is Pig's problem? How does he solve it?
2. Why does it take so many friends to solve the problem?

Write About It

Write about a time you helped a friend.

Working with Words

Phonics

Read the words.

bark	car	far
hard	kind	park
part	sight	stars
try	yard	find

Words to Know

Read the words.

were	or
any	better

Time to Read

Read the story.

Camping in the Yard

Dad and I were camping in the yard. Fluff was with us. He didn't bark or run off. We were all good campers! I didn't miss any of my stuff. It was much better than sleeping inside!

At the Big Park

by Ed Reyes
illustrated by Joy Allen

Last year we went camping for
a week. We packed up the car.
We drove to a big park. It was
far away.

When we got to the park, we picked a camping spot. Then we set up the tent.

Most days we went swimming or boating. What could be better than that?

We went hiking on a trail. We got to see lots of deer. They ran off when we came by. I was glad that we didn't see any snakes!

Each day, we ate yummy
things. It's fun to sit on the
grass and eat. Home seemed
so far away!

The nights were the best part!
The sky was filled with stars. I
made lots of wishes!

I liked sleeping in a tent a lot.
It felt hard. But I didn't mind.

I hope we can go back to
the big park. I made a wish
on a star!

Comprehension Check

Retell

Retell the story.
Use the pictures.

Think About It

1. What do you think the boy wished for?
2. How is camping different from being at home?

Write About It

What would you do if you went camping?

Working with Words

Phonics

Read the words.

for	form	forth
Cory	park	sort
sport	star	yard
car	part	torn

Words to Know

Read the words.

again	because
great	around

Time to Read

Read the story.

Cory's Best Sport

Cory went swimming again! That's because she likes it so much. Cory is a great swimmer. She's the best swimmer around!

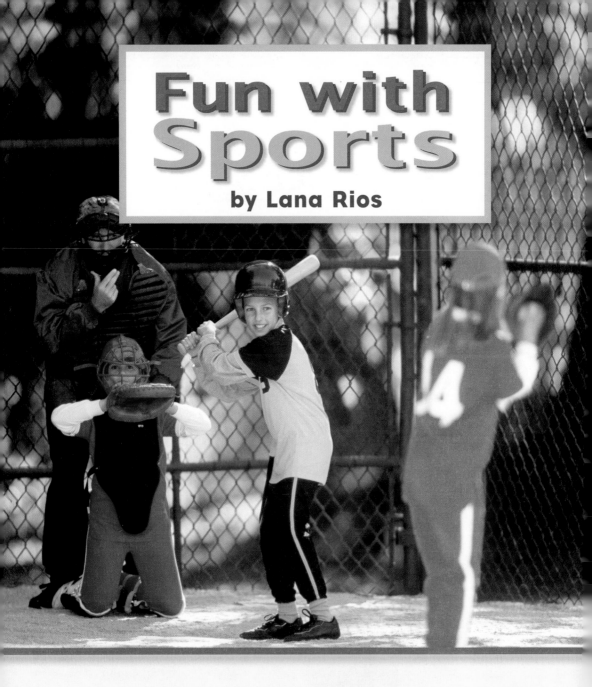

Fun with Sports

by Lana Rios

It's fun to play a sport! Look
at the kids playing baseball. It
is a great sport.

The batter is going to swing. If she misses, she will get a strike. Three strikes and she will be out. The pitcher is trying to get her out!

This player just got a hit.
Then he runs around the
bases. He is a fast runner!
Will he get to home base?

This hitter ran to home plate. He is happy because he just made a home run! His coach and his team are happy, too!

Look at the kids playing soccer. They run back and forth. They kick and pass.

Each team is trying to make a goal. Who will do it?

This player did it! She kicked hard and made a goal. It is a winning goal, and the game is over!

Fans clap for the winning team. Then the two teams shake hands. They are good sports! Next week, they will play again.

Comprehension Check

Retell

Retell the story.
Use the pictures.

Think About It

1. Why does a batter run around the bases?
2. How do you make a goal when you play soccer?

Write About It

Write about a sport that you like to play.

Working with Words

Phonics

Read the words.

bird	perch	chirp
first	form	fern
fur	curb	sports
turn	stir	her

Words to Know

Read the words.

warm	would
from	does

Time to Read

Read the story.

Birds in the Park

It is warm. Would you like to go to the park? We can see birds fly from tree to tree. They chirp a song. A mom feeds her little birds. Does she look after them?
Yes, she does!

Birds' Nests

by Beatrice Reynolds
illustrated by Jenifer Thomas

A bird makes its home in
a nest. Take a look around.
You can find birds' nests in
many spots.

Some birds make their nests in trees or bushes.

Some birds like to make their nests on lakes.

How does a bird make a nest?

This bird makes its nest with twigs and grass. She fills in the holes with mud. The nest will hold her eggs.

This bird made a nest that swings from a branch! She made it with grass, string, and fur.

These birds worked as a team
and made a nest. First, they got
some mud. Then, they pressed
it into big lumps.

This bird made her nest on a lake. She sits on her eggs and keeps them warm.

When the eggs hatch, there will be little birds!

Would you like to help birds?

Get bits of cloth or yarn. Hang them on trees where birds will see them. They will use them for their nests!

Comprehension Check

Retell

Retell the story.
Use the pictures.

Think About It

1. What are the different places where birds build their nests?

2. What different things do birds use to build their nests?

Write About It

Write about the birds you see in your neighborhood.

Working with Words

Phonics

Read the words.

count	cow	crowd
down	first	found
fur	her	now
out	shout	town

Words to Know

Read the words.

once	upon
buy	been

Time to Read

Read the story.

Counting Eggs

Once upon a time, a girl went to buy a hen. She found a fine hen. Each day, it laid ten gold eggs! The girl counted them. "I have never been so lucky!" she said. "But now I am!"

Jack and the Beans

by Steve Gold
illustrated by Mike Wohnoutka

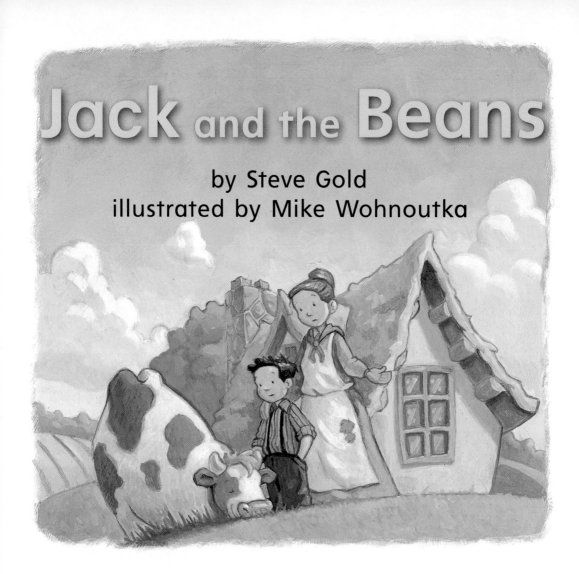

Once upon a time, there was a lad named Jack.

He and his mom lived in a crowded hut. They did not have much. But they had a cow.

Then the cow stopped giving milk.

"Go and sell our cow," Mom told Jack.

So Jack went to town with their cow.

On his way, Jack met a man.

"I will buy this cow for five beans," he told Jack. "The beans will make you rich."

So Jack sold his cow.

He gave his Mom the beans.

"You have been so silly!"
she cried. She threw out the
beans!

The next day, Jack woke
up and saw a big, big plant
outside. It reached the sky!

Jack jumped on the plant and
went up.

At the top, Jack saw ten bags filled with gold.

"I am not greedy. I will take just two bags of gold," said Jack.

And down he went with his gold!

"Mom! Look!" shouted Jack.

"You were right!" cried Mom.

And from that day on, they
had all that they needed!

Comprehension Check

Retell

Retell the story.
Use the pictures.

Think About It

1. Why does Jack take the cow to town?

2. Why does Mom get angry with Jack?

Write About It

What made Jack's beans special?

Working with Words

Phonics

Read the words.

book	cook	good
Snook	out	took
look	town	wood
cow	shook	foot

Words to Know

Read the words.

small	laugh
only	write

Time to Read

Read the story.

My Cat, Snook

Snook is a small cat. But he's very smart. He sits on my lap when I read a book. He looks like he is reading, too. He makes me laugh a lot! Someday, he may be the only cat to write his name.

A Good Birthday

by Beth Lewis
illustrated by Mick Reid

Jean woke up feeling good.
Today was her birthday.

"I hope Mom and Dad got me
a dog!" she said. "That is the
only thing I want!"

Dad was cooking pancakes.

"Happy birthday!" said Mom and Dad.

They ate fast. Then Mom and Dad went to the yard.

Jean went to read her book.
Then she heard loud banging.

She looked out. Mom and Dad
were making something out of
wood.

She went to find out what was going on. She spotted a book.

"Look at this book!" said Jean. She took it out with her.

"What's going on?" Jean asked
Mom and Dad.

"Let's tell her," said Mom.

"We got you a dog!" said Dad.
"He's over there!"

Jean looked. There was a small puppy. She started to laugh.

"That's such a cute dog!" she cried. "I got my wish!"

"Let's think of a name. We will write it on the dog house," said Mom.

"I know!" said Jean. "Let's name him Happy!"

194

Comprehension Check

Retell

Retell the story.
Use the pictures.

Think About It

1. What did you think Jean's parents were building?

2. What other clues told you that there was a dog?

Write About It

Write about a pet that you would like.

Working with Words

Phonics

Read the words.

cool	look	moon
noon	shoot	soon
too	took	wood
stool	room	tooth

Words to Know

Read the words.

full	blue
one	call

Time to Read

Read the story.

The Moon and Stars

Tonight there is a full moon in a dark blue sky. There are many stars, too. One star is the brightest. We call it the North Star. If we are lucky, we'll see a shooting star, too!

The Sun and the Moon

by Raymond Storey
illustrated by Ruth Flanigan

Every morning, the sun rises in the east.

Soon, the dark sky gets light. The sun's light makes the sky look blue.

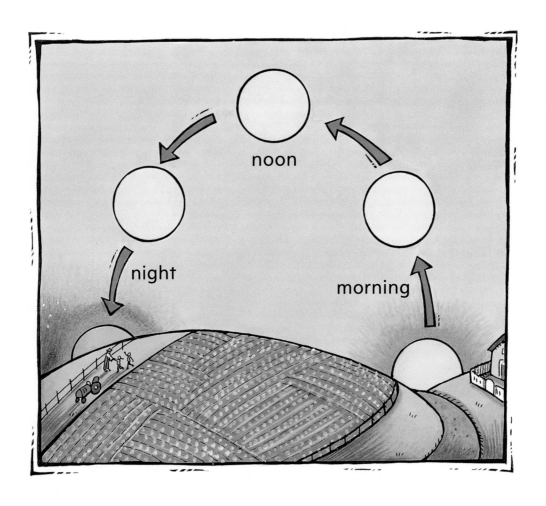

In the morning, the sun is low in the sky. By noon, the sun is high.

At the end of the day, the sun gets lower. Then it sets in the west.

It may seem as if the sun moves in the sky. But it is the earth that moves!

Each day, the earth spins around one time.

As the earth spins away from
the sun, it is night. It is cooler
at night. We can see the moon
and stars in the night sky.

The moon moves around
the earth. That is why it
doesn't always look the same.
Sometimes it is big and round.
We call it a full moon.

Sometimes we can see only part of the moon.

The moon doesn't have any light of its own. It gets its light from the sun.

Did you know that the stars are out all the time?

We can't see them in the daylight. But at night, we can see many stars—too many to count!

Comprehension Check

Retell

Retell the story.
Use the pictures.

Think About It

1. How are the night and day skies different?

2. Why does it get cooler at night?

Write About It

How does the sky look right now? Write what you see.

Working with Words

Phonics

Read the words.

claw	moon	hawk
soon	crawl	paws
saw	jaw	too
fault	fawn	lawn

Words to Know

Read the words.

four	wash
goes	carry

Time to Read

Read the story.

Four Cubs

Four cubs crawl around their mom. She will wash them by licking them clean. She pats them with her paws. Then she goes off to hunt for food. She will carry it back in her jaws.

207

Paws and Claws

by Herb Arkins

How do animals get food? Some use paws and claws. This big cat is hunting. It runs fast on four strong legs.

It will use its claws to help catch food. Then it will use strong jaws and teeth to eat. After eating, it will wash its paws.

This big animal goes up a tree to get its food. It eats nuts and berries and leaves. Sharp claws help it grab the trunk.

A hawk is a good hunter
because it sees very well.
It can swoop down to catch a
little bird. Then it will carry it
off in its claws.

Not all birds use claws to get food. Some use beaks and bills.

This bird has a long, thin beak. It helps it reach inside a plant to get a drink.

This bird has a big bill. It swoops down to catch fish. A big fish can fit in its wide bill.

This bird drills holes in a tree trunk with its hard beak. Inside the tree are good things to eat such as bugs.

Peck, peck, peck means it's time to eat!

Comprehension Check

Retell

Retell the story.
Use the pictures.

Think About It

1. Which animals use claws to get food? Which use beaks?
2. How are a tiger and a bear alike? How are they different?

Write About It

Write about how another animal gets it food.

Working with Words

Phonics

Read the words.

boy	jaws	coin
join	noise	Troy
paws	point	spoil
toy	fault	joy

Words to Know

Read the words.

pretty	open
seven	eight

Time to Read

Read the story.

The Toy Chest

A boy and a girl got a new toy chest. It was big and pretty. Each day, they would open the chest and find a new toy. Soon they had seven games and eight wind-up toys!

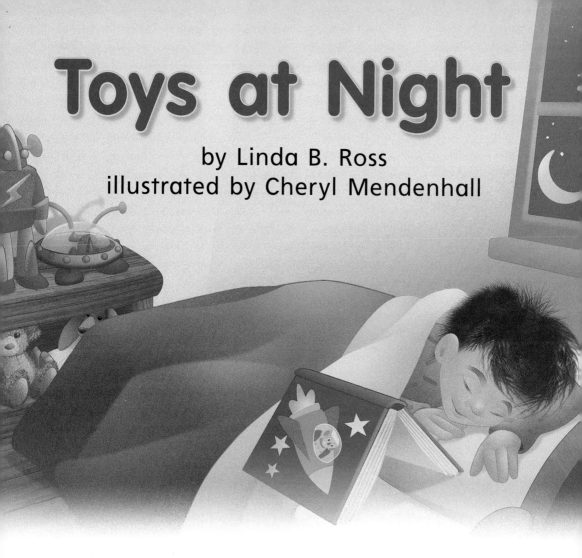

Toys at Night

by Linda B. Ross
illustrated by Cheryl Mendenhall

Troy got into bed.

"I'll read my book before I go to sleep," he said.

But he could not keep his eyes open. Soon he was sleeping.

A while later, a noise woke him up. Troy sat up in bed. He blinked at what he saw.

"Are my eyes tricking me?" he asked.

Troy saw his toy animals
marching around the room.
All seven were marching and
singing.

"This can't be!" he cried.

220

"Why can't it be?" asked Pig.
"Don't you think we can have
fun, too?"

"Well, yes," Troy started
to say.

"We don't move when you are up," the pretty bird told him.

"Well, I don't mean to spoil your fun," said Troy. "I'm just shocked!"

Then his eight robots jumped down from the shelf. They joined the marching line.

"Wow! This is fun!" said Troy.

The next day, Troy got up. His toys did not march or sing. They just sat still.

"Was it just a dream?" he asked. "I hope not!"

Comprehension Check

Retell

Retell the story.
Use the pictures.

Think About It

1. What kinds of toys does Troy have? What can they do?

2. Do you think the toys like day or night better? Why?

Write About It

How might your toys have fun at night?

Skills and Strategies

TITLE	PHONICS	HIGH-FREQUENCY WORDS	COMPREHENSION
Vol.1 Unit 1 pages 6–75			
8 Pam Ran 14 Sam Can Nap	/a/ *a* c<u>a</u>n	and I jump not	Analyze Story Structure: Character and Setting
22 Tag 28 At Bat	/a/ *a* b<u>a</u>t	go too we yes	Analyze Story Structure: Character and Setting
36 Can Jim Fit? 42 Big Max	/i/ *i* d<u>i</u>g	be play run the	Analyze Story Structure: Sequence
50 A Trip! 56 Cris the Crab	/kr/ *cr* <u>cr</u>ab, /dr/ *dr* <u>dr</u>ag, /gr/ *gr* <u>gr</u>in, /tr/ *tr* <u>tr</u>ick	a do good on	Analyze Story Structure: Character and Setting
64 Big Cats 70 Ants, Ants, Ants!	/nd/ *nd* ha<u>nd</u>, /nt/ *nt* a<u>nt</u>, /st/ *st* fa<u>st</u>, /nk/ *nk* si<u>nk</u>	help little very what	Analyze Text Structure: Author's Purpose
Vol.1 Unit 2 pages 76–145			
78 Hop, Frog, Hop! 84 My Mom	/o/ *o* h<u>o</u>p	her my see they	Summarize: Main Idea and Details
92 Jen Helps Rex 98 On the Bed	/e/ *e* b<u>e</u>d	are look no who	Summarize: Retell
106 Fish 112 At the Shop	/sh/ *sh* <u>sh</u>op, fi<u>sh</u> /th/ *th* <u>th</u>in, Be<u>th</u>	for here live many	Summarize: Retell
120 Fun with Drums 126 Big Bud	/u/ *u* f<u>u</u>n	have make to want	Visualize: Sequence
134 Can You Clap? 140 Plip, Plop!	/kl/ *cl* <u>cl</u>ap, /fl/ *fl* <u>fl</u>ip, /pl/ *pl* <u>pl</u>op, /sl/ *sl* <u>sl</u>ip	away me today you	Visualize: Sequence
Vol.2 Unit 3 pages 6–75			
8 Dave and Kate 14 Jake's Cake	/ā/ *a_e* m<u>a</u>k<u>e</u>	all eat said walk	Analyze Story Structure: Character and Setting
22 Snakes, Snakes, Snakes! 28 Kids Can Play	/sk/ *sc* <u>sc</u>ales, /sk/ *sk* <u>sk</u>ate, /sl/ *sl* <u>sl</u>ed, /sn/ *sn* <u>sn</u>ake, /sp/ *sp* <u>sp</u>in	together under was when	Analyze Text Structure: Main Idea and Details
36 Wake Up, Chicks! 42 Let's Eat Lunch	/ch/ *ch* <u>ch</u>ick, bun<u>ch</u>, /ch/ *tch* ca<u>tch</u>, /hw/ *wh* <u>wh</u>en	come our some your	Summarize: Retell
50 Five Ducks and a Frog 56 Miss White's Dime	/ī/ *i_e* d<u>i</u>m<u>e</u>	how now there where	Generate Questions: Make Predictions
64 Stripes, Stripes, Stripes! 70 It's Spring!	/skr/ *scr* <u>scr</u>atch, /spl/ *spl* <u>spl</u>ash, /spr/ *spr* <u>spr</u>ing, /str/ *str* <u>str</u>ipes	three give of put	Generate Questions: Compare and Contrast

TITLE	PHONICS	HIGH-FREQUENCY WORDS	COMPREHENSION
Vol.2 Unit 4 pages 76–125			
78 Mole's Home	/ō/ o_e h_ole_	he into saw soon	Monitor Comprehension: Make Inferences
88 June's Flute	/ū/ u_e m_ule_, fl_ute_	could new she work	Monitor Comprehension: Draw Conclusions
98 Trains, Trains, Trains!	/ā/ ay d_ay_, ai s_ai_l	about know read these	Monitor Comprehension: Compare and Contrast
108 Let's Plant Seeds	/ē/ e b_e_, ee tr_ee_, ea p_ea_ch	after by down kind	Summarize: Main Idea and Details
118 Milly Cleans Up	/ē/ y happ_y_	before done pull two	Summarize: Beginning, Middle, and End
Vol.2 Unit 5 pages 126–175			
128 Three Billy Goats	/ō/ o g_o_, oa g_oa_t, ow sh_ow_	always over their try	Visualize: Fantasy and Reality
138 The Light	/ī/ ind k_ind_, y tr_y_, igh h_igh_	every fall never out	Visualize: Problem and Solution
148 At the Big Park	/är/ ar p_ar_t	any better or were	Generate Questions: Make Inferences
158 Fun with Sports	/ôr/ or sp_or_t	again around because great	Generate Questions: Cause and Effect
168 Birds' Nests	/ûr/ er h_er_, ir b_ir_d, ur f_ur_	does from warm would	Generate Questions: Classify and Categorize
Vol.2 Unit 6 pages 176–225			
178 Jack and the Beans	/ou/ ou c_ou_nt, ow n_ow_	been buy once upon	Summarize: Cause and Effect
188 A Good Birthday	/ů/ oo b_oo_k	laugh only small write	Monitor Comprehension: Make Predictions
198 The Sun and the Moon	/ü/ oo m_oo_n	blue call full one	Summarize: Compare and Contrast
208 Paws and Claws	/ô/ au f_au_lt, aw p_aw_s	carry four goes wash	Monitor Comprehension: Classify and Categorize
218 Toys at Night	/oi/ oi n_oi_se, oy t_oy_	eight open pretty seven	Monitor Comprehension: Use Illustrations

ACKNOWLEDGMENTS

ILLUSTRATIONS

7: Aleksey Ivanoff. 8-12: José Cruz. 14-18: Olga and Aleksey Ivanov. 21: Holly Conger. 36-40: Shari Halpern. 42-26: R.W. Alley. 50-54: Joan Paley. 56-60: Deborah Morse. 70-74: Judith Moffatt. 77: Barry Rockwell. 78-84: Olga and Aleksey Ivanov. 88-94: Carolyn Croll. 97: Chi Chung. 107: Chi Chung. 108-114: Philippa A. Kirby. 117: Amy Huntington. 118-124 Cathy Morrison. 127: Gideon Kendall. 128-134: Barry Rockwell. 137: Peter Whitehead. 138-144: John Wallner. 147: Joy Allen. 148-154: Joy Allen. 157: Meredith Johnson. 167: Amy Huntington. 168-174: Jenifer Thomas. 177: Peter Whitehead. 178-184: Mike Wohnoutka. 187-194: Mick Reid. 198-104: Ruth Flanigan. 207: Amy Huntington. 218-224: Cheryl Mendenhall.

PHOTOGRAPHY

All photographs are by Macmillan/McGraw Hill (MMH) except as noted below:

3: PhotoLink/Getty Images; 5: Alan and Sandy Carey/Getty Images; 22: (l) John Cancalosi/age FOTOSTOCK; (r) Don Vail/Alamy; (bkgd) Siede Preis/Getty Images; 23: (t) Siede Preis/Getty Images; (bkgd) Siede Preis/Getty Images; 24-25: (t) Paul Chesley/Getty Images; (bkgd) Siede Preis/Getty Images; 25: © Peter Arnold, Inc./Alamy; 26: (t) Michael & Patricia Fogden/CORBIS; 28: © AM Corporation/Alamy; 29: (t) Carson Ganci/Pixtal/AGEfotostock; 30: (t) Steve Skjold/Photo Edit; 31: © Kathy Ferguson-Johnson/ Photo Edit; 32: © Karl Weatherly/Photodisc/Getty Images; 64: (l) Siede Preis/Getty Images; (c) Brand X Pictures/PunchStock; (r) PhotoLink/Getty Images; 65: PhotoLink/Getty Images; 66: © Dr Maurice G Hornocker/National Geographic/Getty Images; 67: © Chris Rout/Alamy; 68: © IT STOCK INT'L/eStock Photo/PictureQuest; 98: SuperStock; 99: © Pixtal/SuperStock; 100: © Photofusion Picture Library/Alamy; 101: © Frances Roberts/Alamy; 102: © Simon Crofts/Alamy; 103: © age fotostock/SuperStock; 104: © Robert W. Ginn/Photo Edit; 158: Zoran Milich/Masterfile; 159: © Jim Cummins/CORBIS; 160: Dennis MacDonald/ AGE Fotostock; 161: Terry Vine/Stone/Getty Images; 162: © David Young-Wolff/Photo Edit; 163: © Charles Gupton/CORBIS; 164: © Richard Hutchings/Photo Edit; 208: Alan and Sandy Carey/Getty Images; 209: Tom Vezo/Peter Arnold, Inc.; 210: © blickwinkel/Alamy; 211: © Eric and David Hosking/CORBIS; 212: Ingram Publishing/AgeFotostock; 213: (c) David Tipling/Alamy; 214: Millard H. Sharp/Photo Researchers, Inc.